Tips for Reading Together

Children learn best when reading is fun.

- Talk about the title and the pictures on the cover.
- Discuss what you think the story might be about.
- Read the story together, inviting your child to read as much of it as they can.
- Give lots of praise as your child reads, and help them when necessary.
- Try different ways of helping if they get stuck on a word. For example, get them to say the first sound of the word, or break it into chunks, or read the whole sentence again, trying to guess the word. Focus on the meaning.
- Have fun finding the hidden letters.
- Re-read the story later, encouraging your child to read as much of it as they can.

Children enjoy re-reading stories and this helps to build their confidence.

Have fun!

Find the 7 hidden keys, and the letters and letter shapes that make up the word TRAPPED.

Trapped!

Written by Cynthia Rider
Illustrated by Alex Brychta

OXFORD
UNIVERSITY PRESS

Please return
the key
_____
Keep dogs
on a lead

Gran took the children and
Floppy to see an old castle.

The children went up the path to the castle. Suddenly, Chip stopped.

He pointed to a window at the top.
"Look, there's a face," he said.

Everyone looked, but the face
had gone.

"It can't be a face," said Gran.
"The castle is empty."

They went into the castle.

"It looks very old," said Biff.

"And very scary!" said Kipper.

"Let's play hide and seek," said
Chip.

The children ran in and out of
the rooms.

"I'll play too," said Gran, and
she went into the next room.

Gran looked for a place to hide.
She saw a gate and pulled it open.

CLANG! The gate banged shut.
Gran pushed it, but it was stuck.
"Help! Help!" she shouted.

The children ran to see what had happened.

"I'm trapped," said Gran.

The gate was very stiff.
The children pulled and pulled.
At last, it opened.

"I'll keep the gate open with this old chest," said Gran. "I don't want to be trapped again."

"Come on," said Kipper. "Let's see where these stairs go."

They all went up the stairs.

Suddenly, they heard a noise.
Woo...ooo! WOO...OOO!
"What was that?" said Biff.

The noise came again.

Woo...ooo! WOO...OOO!

Floppy pulled at his lead and raced up the stairs.

"Come on! We must go after Floppy," said Chip. They all ran to the top of the stairs.

Floppy was scratching at a small
door. Gran slowly turned the
handle.

They saw a small dusty room.

"Come on, Floppy," said Biff.

"Let's have a look around."

Something went flapping across
the room.

"What's that?" said Biff.

Chip pointed. "It's an owl," he whispered. "It must be the face I saw at the window."

"Poor thing! It must have come down the chimney," said Gran. She picked it up very gently.

Gran took the owl over to the
window and opened it. The owl
blinked its big round eyes.

"Go on, owl," said
Kipper. "Fly away!"
The owl flapped
its wings and flew
up into the sky.

Kipper watched the owl fly away. "It must be horrible to be trapped," he said.

"It is, Kipper," said Gran. "It is!"

Think about the story

Why did Chip think he had seen a face at the window?

Why did Gran call to the children for help?

Why did Gran keep the gate open with the chest?

What would you do if you found a trapped animal?

Rhyming pairs

Find the four pairs of things that rhyme.
Which is the odd pair out?

**Useful common words repeated in this story and
other books in the series.**
again   children   help   look(ed)   must   play   pulled
something   suddenly   that   very   went   what('s)
Names in this story: Biff   Chip   Gran   Kipper   Floppy

More books for you to enjoy

Level 1:	Level 2:	Level 3:	Level 4:	Level 5:
Getting Ready	Starting to Read	Becoming a Reader	Building Confidence	Reading with Confidence

OXFORD
UNIVERSITY PRESS

Great Clarendon Street,
Oxford OX2 6DP

Text © Cynthia Rider 2006
Illustrations © Alex Brychta 2006

First published 2006
All rights reserved

Series Editors: Kate Ruttle,
Annemarie Young

British Library Cataloguing
in Publication Data available

ISBN–13: 978-019-279236-5

10 9 8 7 6 5 4 3

Printed in China by Imago

Have more fun with Read at Home